Mandi and Her Dad Go Shopping

Pamela Graham

Illustrated by Liz Dixon

Mandi and her dad go shopping.

Along the street,

through the park,

and over the bridge,

Mandi and her dad go shopping.

Up the hill,

around the corner,

and past the post office,

Mandi and her dad go shopping.

Past the florist,

past the bookstore,

and past the coffee shop,

Mandi and her dad go shopping.

5

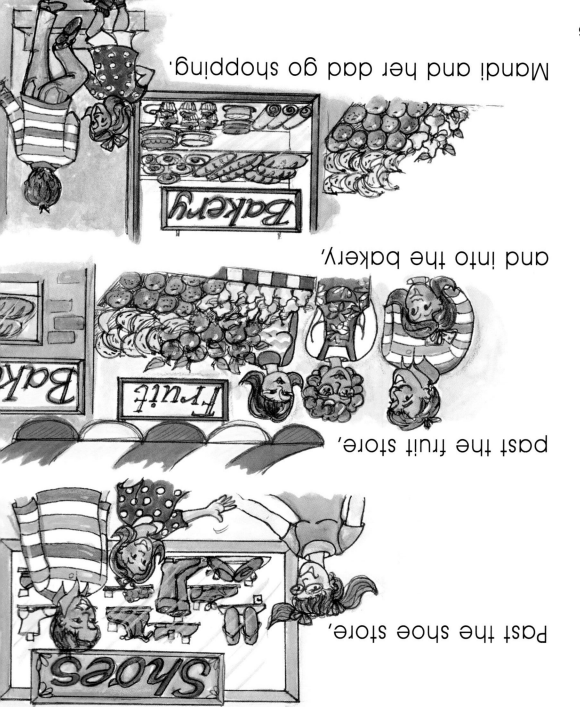

Mandi and her dad go shopping.

and into the bakery.

past the fruit store,

Past the shoe store,

Past the bread,

past the cookies,

and up to the counter,

Mandi and her dad go shopping.

And they buy the biggest birthday cake
in the store.